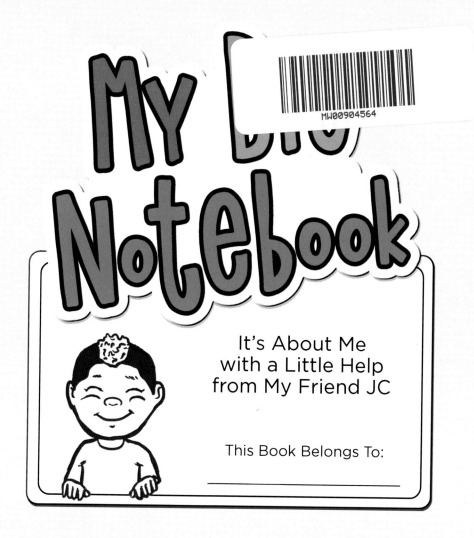

My Big Notebook

It's About Me
with a Little Help
from My Friend JC

This Book Belongs To:

_____

By JC and Carla Carlisle
Illustrated by Quadasia Prescod

SPARK Publications
Charlotte, NC

**My Big Notebook: It's About Me with
a Little Help from My Friend JC**
By JC and Carla Carlisle
Illustrated by Quadasia Prescod

Designed, produced, and published by SPARK Publications
SPARKpublications.com
Charlotte, North Carolina

Printed in the United States of America.
Paperback, October 2021, ISBN: 978-1-953555-14-4
Library of Congress Control Number: 2021916821

JUVENILE NONFICTION / Activity Books / General
JUVENILE NONFICTION / Family / Alternative Family
JUVENILE NONFICTION / Social Topics / Emotions & Feelings

My Big Notebook is dedicated to children
all over the world. We created a "buddy
in a book" just for you to have a safe space
to express and process your feelings.
You deserve it.

We love you.
JC & Mom

The purpose of the book is to provide
children with their own space to
understand feelings, get feelings out and
work through emotions, self soothe, and
feel better about themselves.

Note to your adult

I have had the distinct pleasure of working with Carla Carlisle as she traversed one of the greatest challenges a parent can face. The struggles with her son, secondary to severe trauma, brought us together as a team. She invested her emotions and her strength to help a boy grow into a young man, though it took time, sweat, and tears. Many foster parents would have given up, which I have seen professionally numerous times. I have not seen as much kindness in the face of anger, strength in the face of fear, and deep unconditional love as I have seen with Carla. Rarely do I see a parent with as much determination and compassion as I saw with her. The book she has written comes from her life experiences; she has walked the walk and the skills within this book are the steps for you to follow in her success.

This book gives your child the tools to develop insight into their emotions and identifies the most successful coping strategies to get them through it. This not only helps the child learn emotional regulation, but it allows you as the parent to understand them and help point them in the right direction. After emotions are understood, better decisions can be made. As the parent you will need patience. You will have to model emotional stability even in the face of harsh words and actions from your child.

True strength doesn't come from struggling by yourself, rather it comes from recognizing when you need to ask for help. Reaching out to your pediatrician is an excellent start. If you can find a therapist who connects with your child, that's even better. They can be an important sounding board for both you and your child. While many parents hesitate to consider seeking a child psychiatrist, some children will struggle greatly without the benefit of psychotropic medications. Your pediatrician can help you decide if a referral is necessary. If in doubt, start the referral, since the wait for an appointment in many states can be months away. The vast majority of children will recover with unconditional love. You can change a child's life with enough patience and the right intentions.

-Dr. Tatum, D.O.
Child and Adolescent Psychiatrist

My name is JC. I am in elementary school and live with my Mommy. Things are not always easy for me, so I have a few special people I talk to. I talk to a lady called Miss J, my therapist, and Mrs. Q. Together with Mommy, we are figuring things out.

I will share a few things they taught me. I am still learning, but maybe it will help you.

My therapist told me about this triangle:
Thoughts, Feelings, and Actions.

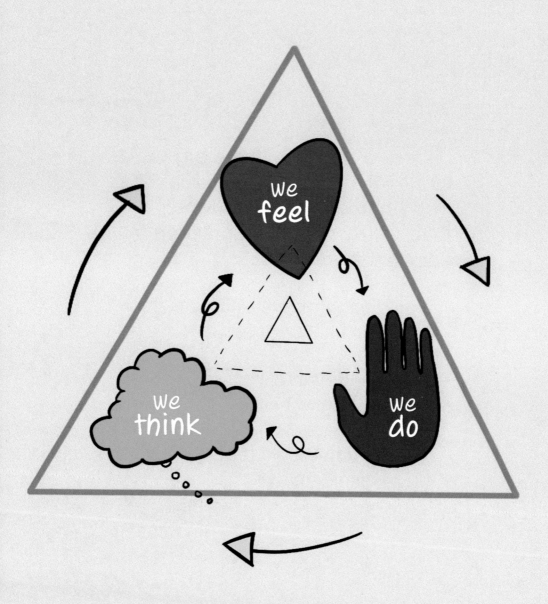

I learned that it is like a big circle. (They call it a cycle, but whatever!) My thoughts lead to my feelings, and then I act on them.

Thoughts are what pop into your head.

 **Feelings** are what is in your heart.

Actions are the things that you do.

Feelings

Thoughts

Actions

I learned about something called "triggers" and the kinds of actions they can cause: fight, flight, or freeze. Some of my friends run or freeze up, but I am a fighter.

triggers

A trigger makes me remember something really tough, bad, or sad that happened.

I'm gonna try to explain.

Sometimes, when I remember something really scary or super sad, my stomach and head start to hurt. Then I get MAD like a fire-breathing dragon! I see RED and just want to hit something.

It happened when I was playing football. My coach did not pick me as a starter, and it made me mad. Football is one of my favorite things in the world to do! I got so mad that I swung my helmet and hurt one of my teammates by accident! He turned out to be okay, but he was so scared. And I was scared too.

Feelings

Thoughts

Actions

What am I doing? I love my teammates and football! I did not want to hurt anybody. I started with a thought from my triangle, "I should be a starter at football, but I am not good enough." Then I felt bad and super mad, and then I acted.

I swung my helmet in anger, but it did not help anything. After talking to Coach Junie and Mommy, the truth was I did not feel good enough. And it made me mad. Mad is easier than sad or disappointed. Kind of.

It happened at home too. One day I wanted some ice cream. I just wanted it. I did not care if I already had dessert and I had to go to bed because it was late. I started saying really bad words to my mom. I did not care! I was super-duper mad! I was going to get my ice cream.

I fussed, cried, and yelled. I even hit the wall with my fist! First, my mom spoke to me sternly. I knew I was in trouble, but I just could not stop!

Then she tried to be nice and kind and then tough. I did not care about any of it! I even tried to take it and run! That did not go well.

My mom tried everything, but I just wanted my ice cream. Mommy finally got me to be still and told me to breathe and count to ten. I did it so fast just to get it over with . . .1, 2, 3, 4, 5. . .10 and done. But still no ice cream!

Mommy just said we are going to do this together. She said, "Let us do square breathing. It will reset our brains and help us settle down. It goes like this. . ."

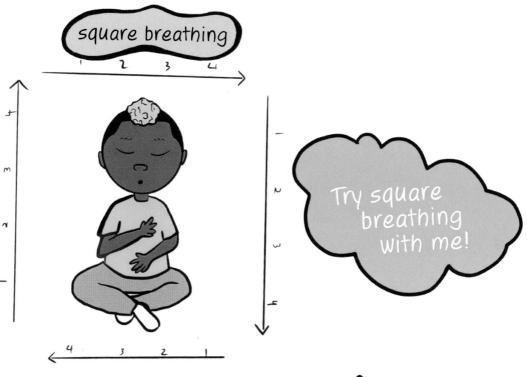

I could not believe it really worked! I relaxed even though I finally knew I wasn't getting my ice cream at bedtime.

We talked about the triangle.

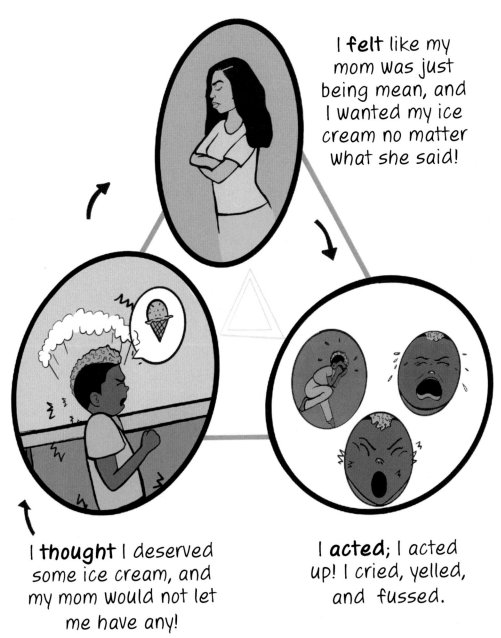

I **felt** like my mom was just being mean, and I wanted my ice cream no matter what she said!

I **thought** I deserved some ice cream, and my mom would not let me have any!

I **acted**; I acted up! I cried, yelled, and fussed.

But my actions did not work. I didn't get my ice cream. Mom was still concerned. She didn't realize that I calmed down. I understand that I have to change things up.

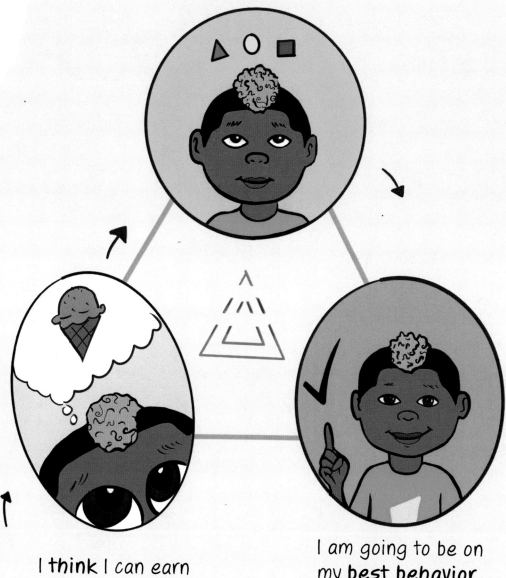

After square breathing and working through my thoughts, feelings, and actions, I was super tired.

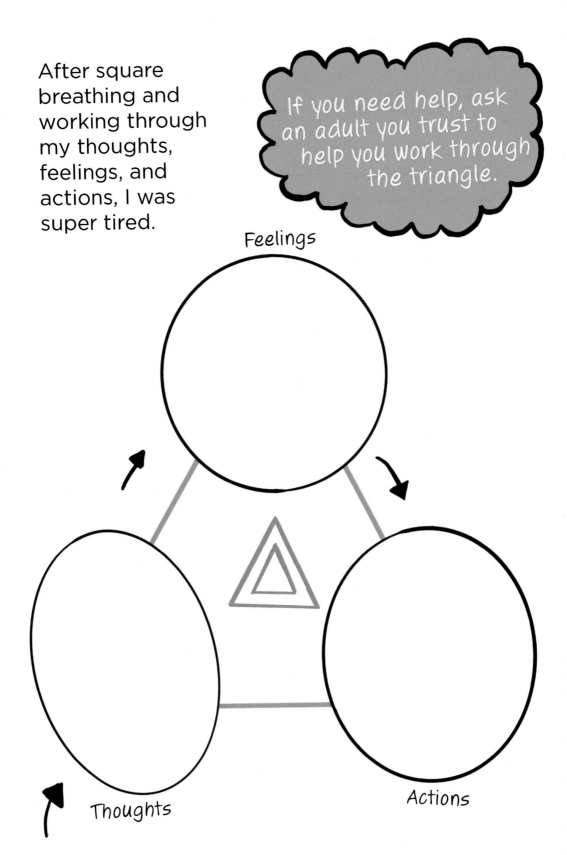

If you need help, ask an adult you trust to help you work through the triangle.

Feelings

Thoughts

Actions

Guess what I did next? I talked to my mom, and I said I was sorry. I was asleep in no time!

I have a cool therapist, Miss J. We do fun things like record raps about my feelings on my phone. It helps me get out feelings I don't like to talk about.

My mom and Miss J made a Chill-Out Spot for me. I could write, sit, pout, and I had pictures of all of my moods.

Where is a spot you can go and just chill out? What can you do or think about to help you feel better?

They taught me to use words to say what I was feeling. And man oh man, that felt great!

Here are what my moods looked like.

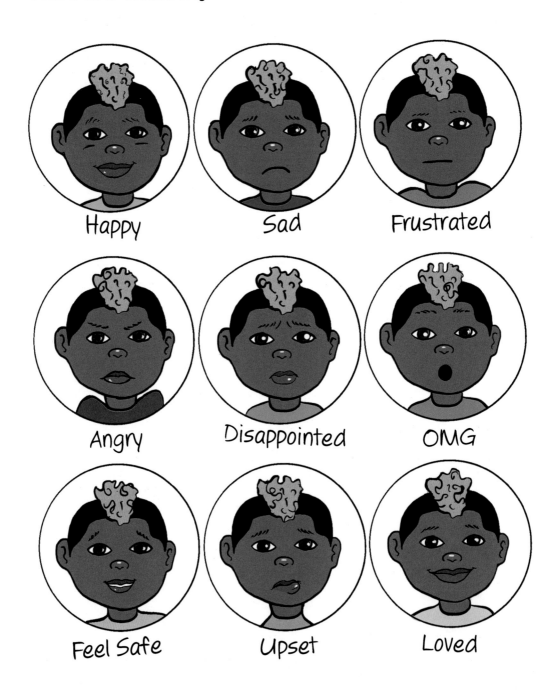

Happy   Sad   Frustrated

Angry   Disappointed   OMG

Feel Safe   Upset   Loved

Seeing my feelings helps me deal with them. I see what I feel now (mad) and the way I want to feel (happy). I can see my feelings! So cool!

Now - Angry

Later - Loved

What are your feelings:

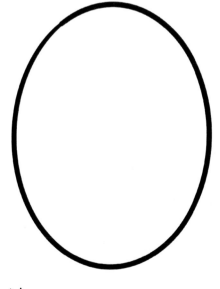

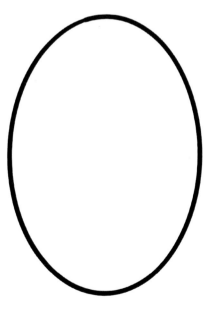

Now - _____

Later - _____

Well, I am learning. I am learning more ways to feel better about myself and handle my feelings. Now that I can say how I feel, it helps me to deal with it. I do mess up sometimes because, hey, I'm human.

The great news is that I spend a lot more time doing fun things because I do not get so mad all the time. I ask for help with my feelings when I think I am going to explode! So it does not happen too much. One day I will be a pro at it!

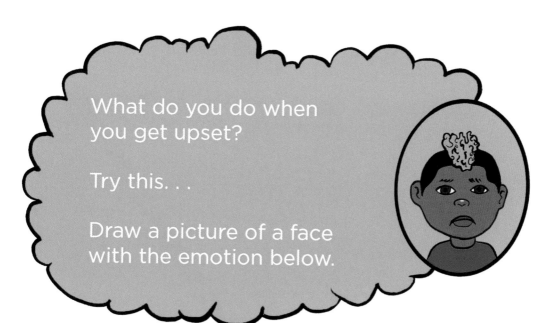

What do you do when you get upset?

Try this. . .

Draw a picture of a face with the emotion below.

What color is each emotion to you? Draw your face using that color if you have a crayon. If you do not, just write in the name of the color.

Sad

Happy

Mad

Excited

Scared

Safe

Upset   Calm

CarlaACarlisle.com

Disappointed

Comfortable

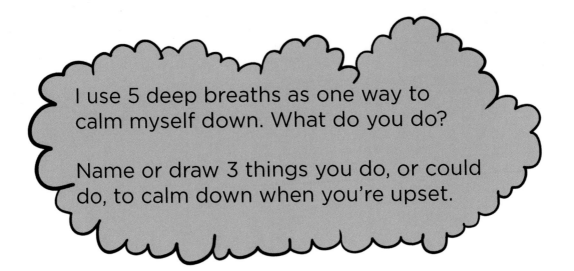

I use 5 deep breaths as one way to calm myself down. What do you do?

Name or draw 3 things you do, or could do, to calm down when you're upset.

Mrs. Q. looks out for me, but she's not always around. I use square breathing to relax and think more clearly. Remember what that looks like?

What is something you do to feel comfy-cozy by yourself?

I really do not like to write that much, because my handwriting is not that great. But the more I practice, the better it gets. Writing helps me see my feelings.

Write a few sentences about how you feel right now.

Where is your favorite place to be?

I love the beach!

When I am frustrated, I close my eyes and think about the beach. There is water and cool waves.

I love the sound of the waves crashing into people. I remember when waves knocked my mom over! It was so funny. She laughed and laughed even though she couldn't see because the water got in her eyes, nose, and mouth!

I like making sand castles.

Use the space below to write or draw a favorite place. It can be pretend or real.

Just something that makes you smile!

Where is your favorite place to be?

When I am frustrated, I...

I love...

_____
_____
_____
_____

I like...

_____
_____
_____

My mom tells me to say my affirmations. I do not always want to, because I do not always feel like they are true. Mom says "fake it until you make it!" I did not even know what that meant. She says the more I say it, the more I will believe it.

Here are my affirmations.
Say them with me!

I am kind.

I am smart.

I am beautifully and perfectly made.

I am a good student.

I am loved.

I am respectful.

I am smart.

I am kind.

I am beautifully and perfectly made.

I am loved.

I am a good student.

I am respectful.

CarlaACarlisle.com

What are some affirmations you could say?

Write at least 5 affirmations below.

I do not always get along with
other kids. Sometimes I feel lonely.
Mom said helping other people can
make me feel better. I feel good
when I hold the door open for
my classmates. My teacher said I
have good manners.

What could you do to help someone else?

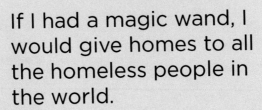

If I had a magic wand, I would give homes to all the homeless people in the world.

What is something amazing you would do if you had a magic wand?

Write it or draw it below.

This next part is all about

YOU!

Write or draw the topic at the top. . . or whatever you want!

This is YOUR notebook!

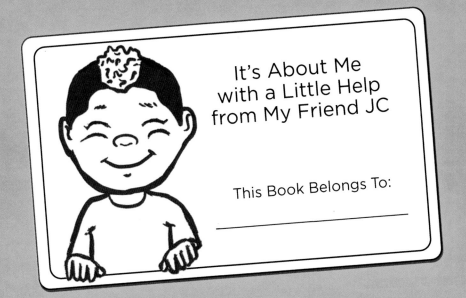

It's About Me with a Little Help from My Friend JC

This Book Belongs To:

_____

What I like about me...

Color in the circles!

My favorite food is...

Color in the scene!

CarlaACarlisle.com

Draw your own pictures!

Color in the circle however you would like.

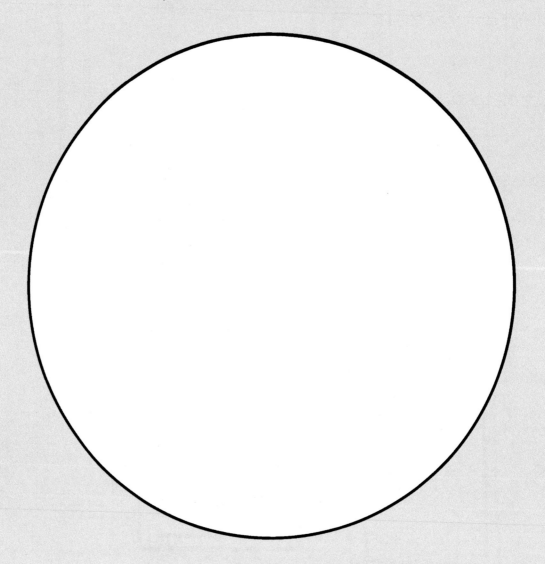

Draw your favorite outside activity.

When I am not happy, I...

Draw a self-portrait!

When I
am alone, I...

Create a poster
using an affirmation!

Hint - if you need help to remember
affirmations, see page 40.

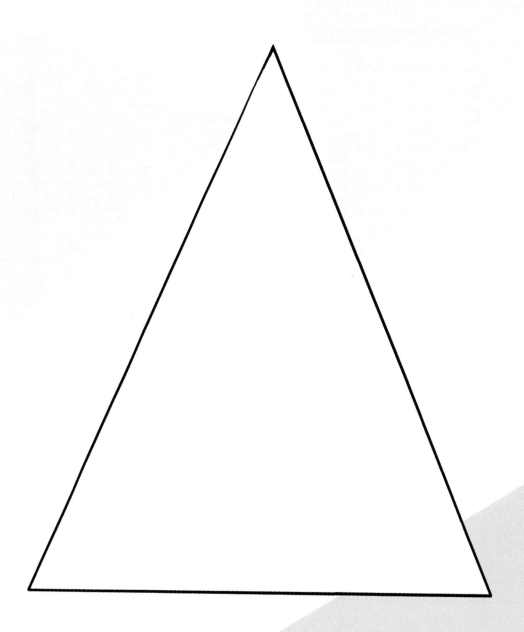

Color or write in the triangle however you would like.

I feel...

Draw your own pictures!

CarlaACarlisle.com

Color in the squares!

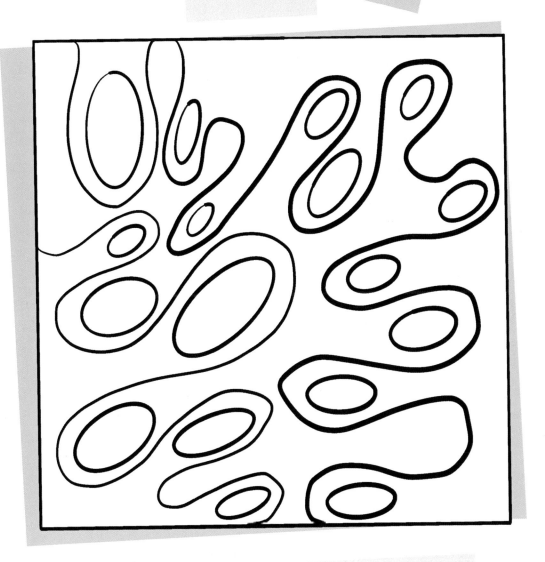

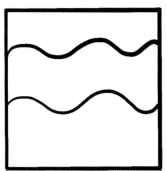

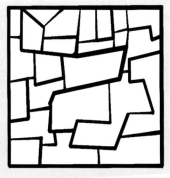

My favorite thing is...

_____
- -
_____
_____
- -
_____
- -
_____
- -
_____
- -
_____
- -
_____
- -
_____

Create a poster!

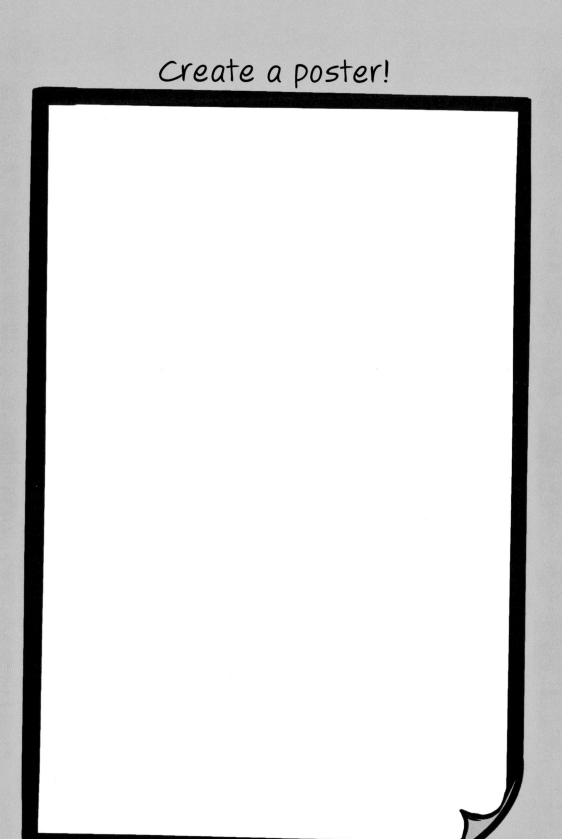

Color in the triangle!

When I am alone, I...

Free draw

Decorate your space!

I want to...

Draw your own pictures!

My happy thoughts are...

-
-
-
-
-
-
-

My super big
dream is...

Color in the scene!

Decorate your space!

Free draw

Color in the squares!

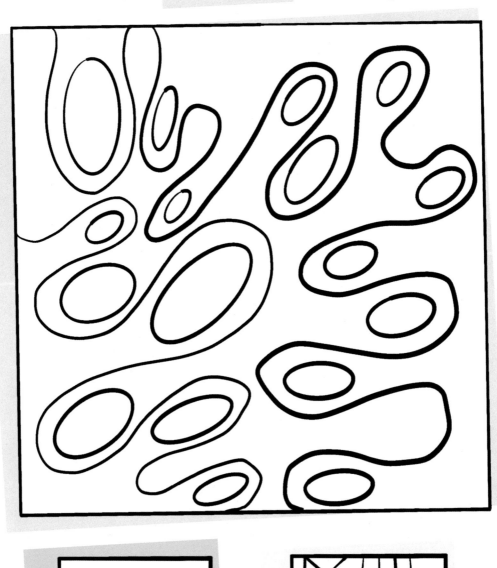

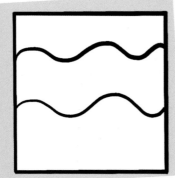

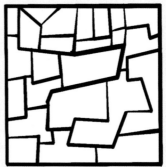

When I am not happy, I...

-

-

-

-

-

-

-

How did I do today?

Thoughts, Feelings, Actions

△ ◯ ▢

___

___

___

Today I...

_____ _____

_____ _____

My happy thoughts are...

Create a poster!

My favorite thing is...

Color in the circles!

Fill in
the square!

CarlaACarlisle.com

Free draw

Fill in the triangles!

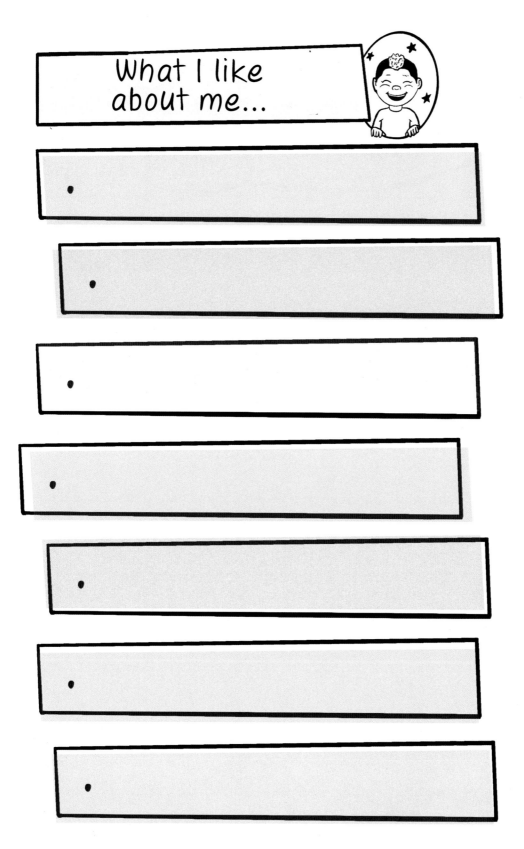

What I like about me...

-
-
-
-
-
-
-

I love to...

Free draw

Color in the circles!

Create a poster
using an affirmation!

Hint - if you need help to remember
affirmations, see page 40.

When I am alone, I...

Fill in
the circle!

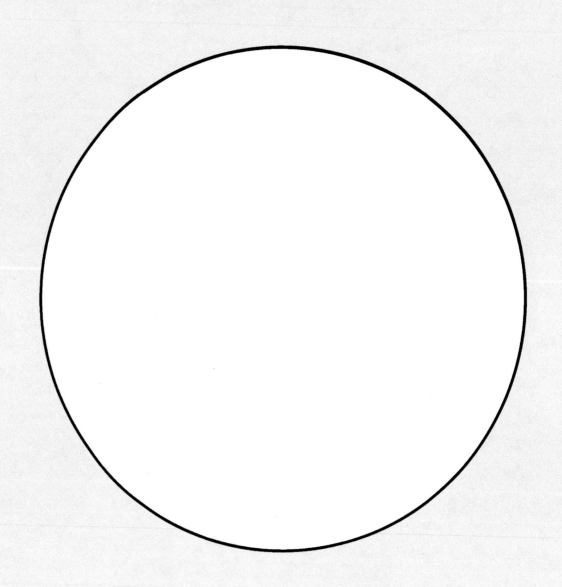

CarlaACarlisle.com

My happy thoughts are...

Draw a self-portrait!

Fill in the triangle!

When I am not happy, I...

Color in the squares!

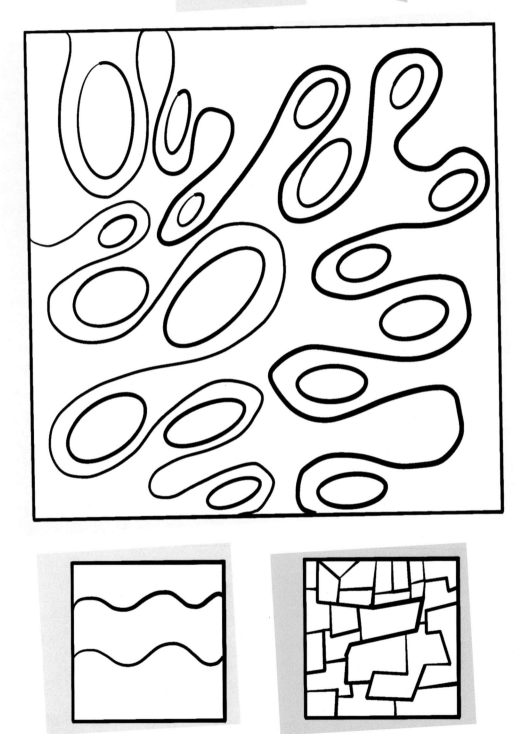

CarlaACarlisle.com

Create a poster using an affirmation!

Hint - if you need help to remember affirmations, see page 40.

How did I do today?

Thoughts, Feelings, Actions

Today I...

My super big
dream is...

Thanks for hanging out
with me for a while to
talk about our feelings!

Do not forget to breathe!

About the Author

Carla Carlisle is an author, mental health advocate, and TEDx Speaker. She serves on the board of the Alexander Children's Foundation, Family Advisory Board of the Duke/UCLA ASAP Center, Policy & Advocacy Committee at MHA of Central Carolinas, and volunteers with NAMI Charlotte. She is the proud recipient of MHA's 2020 Advocacy Award and Mecklenburg County's Crisis Intervention Team (CIT) Team Member of the Year Award (2020).

She speaks, moderates panels, and advocates for becoming trauma informed, ending the stigma of mental illness, and empowering our children who have been impacted by trauma. Generational health is the goal!

Carla earned her bachelor's in sociology from Indiana University. She earned a master's in human resources management from American University and another in organizational development from Johns Hopkins University. Carla obtained a graduate certificate in change management from Johns Hopkins University. She holds multiple certificates, including trauma informed training, Question Persuade Respond (QPR for suicide prevention), Mental Health First Aid, and serves as a mental health storyteller. Carla is a member of Alpha Kappa Alpha, Sorority, Incorporated.

Carla penned her memoir, *Journey to the Son*, to prompt discussions about the lasting, often perilous, impact of trauma many children experience as well as the importance of becoming trauma informed and focused on our mental health.

Most importantly, Carla is a mom who is always learning ways to best care and advocate for mental health, her children, and those who have not yet found their voice.

JC, Junior Editor

JC is a preteen who not only survived extensive Adverse Childhood Experiences (ACEs), but he is thriving! He is a very active boy who loves football and Fortnite! He also loves to laugh and joke and is very generous. JC helped mom (Carla A. Carlisle) with editing this book so it would be relevant to elementary school-age children who deal with stress, trauma, or could use help with coping mechanisms.

About the Illustrator

Quadasia Prescod is a freelance multimedia artist with a bachelor's in visual art & design from the illustrious North Carolina A&T State University. Her body of work is inspired by technique and the exploration of different mediums to create stimulating works of art for her viewers. Her art can be found in published books, murals across the country, and even on skin. She's a painter, sculptor, illustrator, muralist, teacher, and all-around maker, who first got her inspiration from the vibrant books she used to read as a child. Quadasia lives out her purpose by producing things that inspire others to create and express themselves, because she believes everyone is an artist, and everyone has a story worth sharing.

Resources for Adults

Monarch: SECU Youth Crisis Center

Available 24/7, 365 days a year, serving ages 6 – 17 years old.
704-206-2342 – Option 8

National Alliance on Mental Illness (NAMI)

nami.org

American Foundation for Suicide Prevention (AFSP)

afsp.org

Suicide Prevention Lifeline

suicidepreventionlifeline.org/help-yourself/youth/

Suicide Prevention Resource Center (SPRC)

sprc.org

Self-Regulation:

childmind.org/article/can-help-kids-self-regulation/

The National Child Traumatic Stress Network (NCTSN)

nctsn.org

Lucy Listens—Support and Mental Health Services for Children and Families

lucydanielscenter.org/outreach/outreach-caregiver-resources/lucy-listens/

Children's Mental Health information on CDC website

cdc.gov/childrensmentalhealth/index.html

Jason Foundation

jasonfoundation.com/youth-suicide/warning-signs

Trevor Lifeline for LGBTQIA+ Youth

1-866-488-7386

"Social Emotional Learning"

We love sydkimyl.com as an example.

JC's Helpful Hints

Learning links:

Sesame Street in Communities

sesamestreetincommunities.org/about-us/

PBS Kids Feelings Games

pbskids.org/games/feelings/

Calming And Relaxation for Kids

www.mightier.com/activity/5-quick-and-easy-calming-relaxation-techniques-for-kids/

Wellbeyond Meditation for Kids

wellbeyond.com/kids

I am smart.

I am kind.

I am beautifully and perfectly made.

I am loved.

I am a good student.

I am respectful.

Important numbers

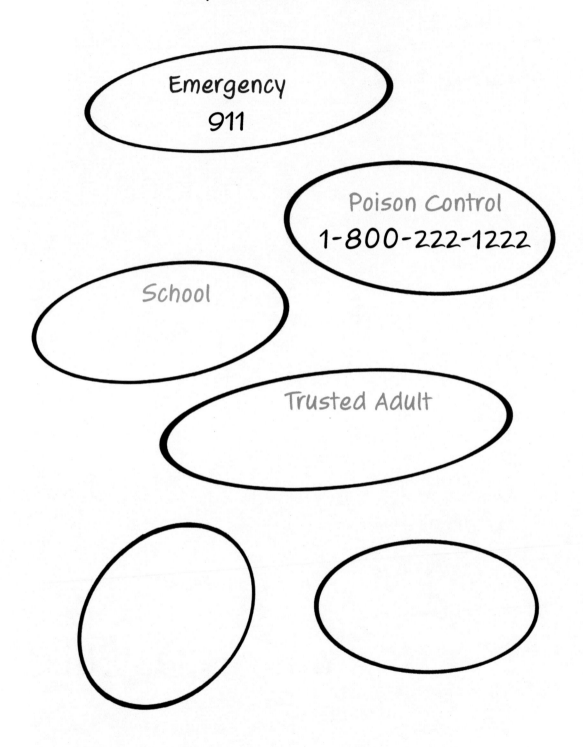

Emergency
911

Poison Control
1-800-222-1222

School

Trusted Adult

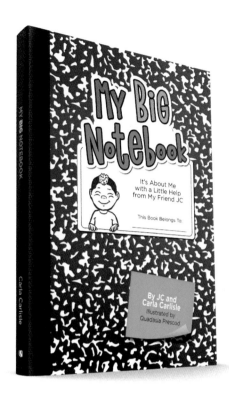

Follow Carla on social media:

CarlaACarlisle

@CarlaACarlisle

Carla A. Carlisle

Carla Carlisle

To order additional copies of
My Big Notebook,
visit CarlaACarlisle.com.

Made in the USA
Columbia, SC
08 March 2022

57185252R00069